ASTROBOTIC AND THE SCRAMBLE TO BEAT NASA BACK TO LUNA.

How a Small Pittsburgh Startup Stunned the Space Industry by Beating NASA Back to the Moon.

Gist Hub

Table of Contents

Chapter 1: We Choose to Go to the Moon.

"We choose to go to the moon in this decade and do the other things, not because they are easy, but because they are hard." When President Kennedy spoke those iconic words in 1962, no one could foresee that less than a decade later, Neil Armstrong would make history by becoming the first human to step foot on the lunar surface. What followed was perhaps humanity's greatest achievement - six successful NASA missions that landed 12 astronauts on the moon between 1969 and 1972.

America held its breath as it huddled around grainy television screens, witnessing these brave explorers bounding across the gray, powdery regolith, Earth visibly suspended in the black sky above. People around the world felt united and overflowing with pride at what humans could accomplish through science and engineering. The Apollo missions signaled the peak of American exceptionalism and spaceflight supremacy.

And then, it stopped. Despite further plans to establish a permanent human presence on the moon, NASA's ambitions were if not abandoned, indefinitely stalled. The last lunar walk was made by Gene Cernan in December 1972, which marked the anticlimactic end of Apollo 17 - humanity's final steps on another world to this day. Why did NASA fail to capitalize on the monumental momentum and goodwill generated by Apollo's success? Quite simply, we lost interest. With the space race decisively won following the moon landings, the enormous taxpayer funds required for these missions became politically untenable.

A combination of "mission accomplished" complacency within NASA and shifting national priorities turned attention and budgets elsewhere. The heyday of ambitious human space exploration faded from memory as the decades passed, as if humanity's tenure on the moon had all been a fleeting dream. Of course, unmanned probes and telescopes continued revealing and unraveling lunar secrets from afar - but boots on the ground it was not. A lingering sense permeated successive generations that one of humanity's seminal achievements had been left unfinished for reasons they struggled to comprehend.

The moon, which through the Apollo missions had briefly blazed at the very forefront of culture and geopolitics, once again receded from public imagination and policy considerations. NASA's sights were set closer to low-Earth orbit, focusing for the next 50 years on missions to Earth-circling space stations, planetary science, and space telescopes. Attempts to reignite momentum for crewed lunar exploration programs like Constellation sputtered in Congress and failed to launch. It seemed America's political will to lead a return was missing.

However, the moon did not relinquish its hold on our dreams. As the 21st century progressed, at first gradually and then precipitously, there came a global resurgence of interest in lunar exploration - and the feeling that Apollo had left unfinished business. The rise of private space companies eager to fill the gap left by risk-averse government programs coincided with several space agencies committing to accelerate plans for renewed moon missions. India, Japan, Europe, Russia, and China all made clear their intentions to pursue both robotic and human lunar exploration over the coming decades.

Most ambitiously, China continues marching toward crewed landings and has openly stated its long-range goal of establishing a permanent, continually crewed lunar base. With little transparency over China's progress and timelines, this lit a fire under American leaders who suddenly faced the prospect of China supplanting US supremacy on the very celestial soil where American astronauts had trod decades prior. Combined with a swelling tide of domestic support for new Apollo-esque national missions of discovery, the stage was set in the early 2020s for the United States to announce its decisive return to the moon.

The Artemis Program, named after Apollo's mythological twin sister, represents humanity's first steps toward establishing a sustained human presence on the lunar surface. NASA is spearheading an ambitious timetable to land astronauts on lunar soil by 2024 and establish a permanent moon base soon thereafter. But unlike Apollo, Artemis takes a fundamentally collaborative approach - uniting international partners and private industry to pool resources and know-how. The extensive complexities and risks inherent in not just reaching the moon but learning to live and work on its surface for months at a time cannot fall to NASA and American taxpayers alone. This time, we go to the moon together - as a species.

Chapter 2: The Commercial Space Race

While NASA's renewed efforts to return astronauts to the lunar surface has fueled excitement worldwide, equally important is the parallel rise of private space companies aiming to unlock the moon's immense potential. This commercial space race has expanded beyond the flagship billionaire-backed ventures of SpaceX and Blue Origin to include dozens of entrepreneurial startups vying to carve roles in cis-lunar enterprise. Corporations large and small alike foresee profitability in providing services to support sustained lunar exploration and industrialization. In the process, they hope to own pieces of a futuristic off-world economy encompassing tourism, mining, manufacturing, infrastructure, media, and real estate.

The prospect of accessing the moon's considerable natural resources, including precious metals, oxygen, and titanium, underpins much commercial interest. But despite limited geological surveys, the viability and business models for lunar mining remain uncertain. More immediately attractive is using the moon's ultra-cold permanently shadowed craters to extract water ice - valuable not just for sustaining human habitats but also for splitting into rocket fuel. For all space-faring operations, transporting mass off of Earth's deep gravity well incurs tremendous launch costs. The ability to manufacture spacecraft, habitats, tools, and fuel using local lunar resources could transform the equation for deep space exploration to Mars and beyond.

Thus the moon offers abundant business opportunities on two fronts - serving NASA's Artemis timeline as a contractor for various operational needs, while also laying the groundwork for whatever space economy may blossom once a sustained human footprint is established. The emerging cis-lunar ecosystem interlinks both government and commercial enterprises in a public-private collaborative unlike what powered the Apollo moonshots. Contracts and partnerships for developing lunar landers, rovers, habitats, spacesuits, experiments, communications, logistics services and more have been awarded across the nascent industry.

Leading the commercial pack is SpaceX which was awarded a $3 billion contract to develop Starship HLS as NASA's first crewed lunar lander since Apollo. While an aggressive timeline makes a 2024 touchdown unlikely, the very prospect of Elon Musk's colossal rocket one day ferrying astronauts between lunar orbit and the surface makes SpaceX early frontrunners. Blue Origin and Dynetics also won initial human lander contracts from NASA, but SpaceX remains farthest in development of flight-ready hardware. Separately, SpaceX envisions Starship eventually enabling space tourism jaunts around the moon later this decade as it works towards Mars ambitions.

Flying under the radar is Pittsburgh startup Astrobotic which focuses solely on delivering payload to the lunar surface. By keeping to an unmanned, minimalist design for its Peregrine lander, Astrobotic attracted extensive commercial interest across dozens of countries and companies aiming to book a cube satellite's worth of space aboard Peregrine's first mission in 2024. One academic researcher even coordinated a student contest to decide what memento poster to fly representing the people of Earth. Astrobotic's lunar delivery service model eschews men and missions in favor of maximizing flexibility for its global customer base within modest budgets.

Also drawing private sector attention are NASA's recent requests for proposals to develop and deploy lunar terrain vehicles. Who wins these rover contracts will be responsible for facilitating extended astronaut exploration across wider swaths of lunar geography. From Audi to Toyota, traditional automakers are joining aerospace rivals in next-gen concept designs that reimagine the Apollo-era Lunar Roving Vehicle. Ever more complex self-driving functionality may one day allow customized terrestrial cars converted for the moon to provide astronauts routine transit without EVAs. Lunar roads and racing leagues could spawn an off-world remake of Route 66 Americana culture.

On the infrastructure front, startups like Relativity Space and Icon are vying to leverage proprietary 3D printing and robotics techniques to automate off-world construction of bases, roads, landing pads, blast walls, and other fortifications from basalt nanomaterials or liquefied lunar regolith. Tools perfected on the moon would underpin plans for settler habitats on Mars as humanity pushes outward. Even lunar apparel is drawing innovators who question why spacesuits must remain restricted to bulky 1970s mission profile aesthetics. Next-gen designs target consumer markets with sportswear-inspired pressure suits for that eventual first starlight stroll.

No one can predict which companies will still stand and what services will thrive decades down the road. But the reinvigorated entrepreneurial space economy ensures NASA will not alone define humanity's rekindled affair with Luna this century. Just as aviation and aerospace firms competed in early efforts that eventually manifested today's airline and tourism industries, nascent steps on the part of profit-seekers today blast open an infinite realm of possibilities. As an accessible celestial harbor just three days from Earth, Luna Cape awaits its Kennedy Space Center moment. Those able to uniquely harvest opportunities from coupling with state-sponsored goals today will steer the horizons for private citizens tomorrow.

Chapter 3: Astrobotic Emerges

The NASA contract award to transport the agency's first lunar payloads aboard Astrobotic Technology's Peregrine lander raised some eyebrows back in 2020. Out of the dozen companies selected to deliver science and technology demonstrations to the moon's surface through the Commercial Lunar Payload Services (CLPS) initiative, Astrobotic was perhaps the least well known.

Founded in 2007 as a startup spun out of Carnegie Mellon University's Robotics Institute, Astrobotic toiled away in Pittsburgh for over a decade seemingly flying under the radar. While flashier billionaire-backed space firms like SpaceX, Blue Origin and Virgin Galactic seized headlines in the late 2010s, this modest team lacking big budgets or celebrity status focused single-mindedly on one goal – commercially delivering payloads to the moon. Methodically they had advanced development of their minimalist Peregrine lander through NASA and industry partnerships, aiming to be the first American spacecraft to touchdown on Luna's dark side.

Astrobotic pioneered the notion of parcel delivery service pricing for missions to the moon. For just $1.2 million per kilo, Peregrine promised universities, companies, even individuals a cube satellite's worth of cargo capacity destined for Mare Imbrium's grand lava plains. Conceptually akin to FedEx or UPS for Earth orbit destinations like Space Station, Peregrine would open access beyond low-Earth orbit for customers needing lunar data yet unable or unwilling to build their own costly lander.

By winning NASA's CLPS contracts in 2020, Astrobotic beat out longtime industry players like Lockheed Martin, Masten Space, and Intuitive Machines for the privilege of flying some of those first science payloads back to Luna in over 50 years. Why did establishment aerospace giants lose out to this Pittsburgh dark horse? NASA probably couldn't fully grasp Astrobotic's odds for operational success relative to known authorities.

Rather, the agency likely saw immense value in catalyzing traction for a wider commercial ecosystem – one that might organically nurture future SpaceX-scale titans from promising unknowns. Astrobotic represented a high-risk, high-reward gambit. Failure would defer NASA's payload delivery hopes by mere months or a year perhaps. But smashing success could resonate for decades by accelerating fledgling private markets essential to economically sustaining lunar exploration long-term. With billions committed already to traditional contractors for Artemis elements like SLS, Orion and human landers, why not roll some dice with these smaller contracts?

For Astrobotic's founders and team, NASA's bet signified hard-fought validation after years when most dismissed their ambitions as delusional. The company's pragmatic lander design was minimalist by necessity, not ideology. With infinitesimally slim odds of attracting billionaire backers like Bezos or Musk, they focused engineering efforts around maximizing reliability and tolerances using off-the-shelf commercial parts rather than inventing customized technology. Founder John Thorton compared the bootstrap strategy to Southwest Airlines choosing to fly just one aircraft type, or Walmart stocking shelves only with best-selling products, to tightly constrain business complexity.

Astrobotic prioritized fiscal sustainability using services revenue rather than relying on speculative investor funding. Maintaining full ownership was deemed crucial for appointing their chosen risk thresholds. Demand for Luna deliveries existed, although modest; they sought only to profitably satisfy a small slice of that demand, not dominate the entire market. Laser-focus on their core transporter competency led them to skip tangential work on landers, rovers, ISRU, habitats or other thirsty complexities that drained rival startups' resources.

Of course, major tech hurdles still presented themselves on the road towards Peregrine's operationalization. Guidance algorithms ensuring precise targeting of landing sites had to be honed. New thrust power negation and shock absorption techniques were devised to safely cradle payloads during tense terminal descent braking. And the team endlessly simulated potential points of failure across navigational sensors, caching processors, inertial measurement units, altitude detectors, pulsed liquid engines, and other critical flight subsystems.

By the mid 2010s, NASA leadership certainly knew Astrobotic's name if not yet convinced of their credibility. That key early advocate emerged in the form of administrator Jim Bridenstine, himself once a dark horse candidate, who came to champion the Pittsburgh startup's value proposition. When Vice President Pence charged NASA with accelerating Artemis plans in 2019, Bridenstine's support swelled for buying reliability on faster timetables via private partners. The recent success of SpaceX's commercial cargo and crew flights for Station furnished all the proof Bridenstine required. The CLPS contracts soon followed, with Peregrine earning flagship billing.

Far from offended, aerospace incumbents largely welcomed Astrobotics emergence. New players eager to trade stakes in short-term revenue for long-term market growth aligned commercial interests with the prime directive NASA conveyed to industry - catalyze each other's success. And so Astrobotic prepared to earn its shot for Peregrine to leap from America's industrial heartland towards making history 240,000 miles away.

Chapter 4: Building Peregrine

Even with NASA's vote of confidence granting a payload delivery contract slot, daunting work lay ahead for Astrobotic's small team to translate their computerized Peregrine lander dreams into physical flight-ready reality. Lacking an Apollo-era blank taxpayer check or billionaire benefactor's deeper pockets, they faced immense technical and manufacturing hurdles to manifest their minimalist moonship design within lean budgets.

Astrobotic's pragmatic engineering strategy around Peregrine had always centered cost-efficiency - maximizing reliability and performance baselines using commercial off-the-shelf parts rather than investing in customized innovations. What resulted resembled an industrial boom lift truck mated with four long legs not unlike a lunar module. Just don't call it ugly around the engineers; for them Peregrine's drab utilitarian looks reflected prudent beauty.

Structurally, the lander comprised three modular components - the transfer stage, descent stage, and payload stage. The transfer stage's engines and propellant would fire following deployment from the Vulcan Centaur rocket once in trans-lunar trajectory, steering Peregrine on its three-day cruise to circumpolar lunar orbit acquisition. This guidance segment jettisons once payload is already committed to landing.

The iconic legged landing base forming Peregrine's underbelly housed larger pulsed liquid thrusters, cylindrical hydrazine fuel tanks, lithium ion batteries, flight computers, inertial sensors, radar altimeters, and exposed wiring that all had to endure dusty touchdown without damage. Shock absorbing stroke on each spindly leg also squeezed every millimeter of give to cushion payloads as the 5,000kg (with fuel) lander braked from 3,280 feet per second to rest. Late stage redundancy across critical flight systems offered backups should sensor readings conflict or engines cut out.

Finally, nestled between triangular support beams at the apex of those spindly legs sat Peregrine's business end - the cargo bay. Spanning just 15 square feet lined with attachment points, every inch maximized for customers loading boxes, experiments, or manifestations of their lunar dreams. Space held at premium dictated strict volume limits on payloads. An augmented suite of cameras focused primarily downward would provide operators and customers terabytes of high definition landing footage.

Guiding Peregrine's design were lessons Astrobotic's founders studied from Surveyor's 1966 soft landings. Namely, complexity invites vulnerability. Minimizing mission scopes by eliminating crew quarters, life support systems, ascent engines, and other equipment necessary only for roundtrip human transport buys reliability. Flying one-way trips Solo each time, Peregrine chose Mars' Spirit and Opportunity as engineering role models over the lost dreams of Luna and Soviet rovers abandoned decades prior.

But just because Peregrine itself resembled scaffolding on an exposed construction lift rather than a sleek spaceship didn't mean customer payloads could withstand spaceflight stresses unshielded. Temperatures fluctuating hundreds of degrees, vacuum pressure, lunar dust, cosmic radiation, microgravity, volatile vibrations and acoustic shock waves during launch all threatened sensitive prototype technologies. Devising modular container and interface specifications to safeguard contents posed nearly as great a logistical puzzle as readying Peregrine itself to protect them.

Astrobotic's payload engineering team invested countless hours working customer-to-customer mitigating size, mass, battery usage, materials and mounting concerns against dynamic launch loads and thermal environments. NASA science instruments required far less handholding than corporate or academic tech demos lacking spaceflight heritage. Entirely new payload guideline rulebooks were written encapsulating hard-learned best practices. Limiting onboard computers, enforcing sleep modes, and proactively identifying single points of failure grew ever more complex as customers stacked up.

Final pre-shipment checkouts of encased payloads piled up steadily as the big day drew nearer. But on the Peregrine manufacturing front, delays began mounting. Fabrication struggles plagued production of the lander's slender legs and thrust nozzles. Software glitches impacted navigation sensors. Fuel leaks sprang in unwanted places while weld strength tests results fluctuated unpredictably. And worst of all, COVID's lingering industrial slowdowns hampered component deliveries on schedules very unforgiving to slippage.

Each setback required rapid root cause assessment and mitigation so problems wouldn't stack or cascade fatally. Exceptionally long work weeks became the norm at Astrobotics Pittsburgh HQ and manufacturing partners across the country worked round the clock to prevent falling critically behind. By mid 2023, nearly all major hardware production hurdles had been cleared or sufficiently contained as the fully integrated Peregrine lander was shipped to Florida for final launch site testing.

Astrobotic's staff watched careers and life savings literally roll towards the launchpad that July. None harbored illusions that success was guaranteed, but they took proud comfort knowing that every bolt was tightened and line of code checked as humanly possible on budget. Now transcending mere startup grit, their scrappy moonshot gambit sought to channel revered Manhattan Project legacies of their

Pittsburgh home. Underdog hopes can outweigh skies, or at least plant boot prints 240,000 miles away.

Chapter 5: The Payloads

Securing over a dozen customers to fully book cargo capacity aboard Peregrine's maiden lunar voyage required far less convincing than Astrobotic once feared. The company's affordable pricing and payload flexibility attracted buyers from corporations to governments to universities - all keen to leverage the rare ride back to Luna. In total 20 payloads were manifested, split between NASA's delivery contracts and other commercial clients.

Headlining Peregrine's payload roster were the five NASA science instruments selected as part of the agency's $250 million Commercial Lunar Payload Services (CLPS) initiative. As hourglass sands trickled towards hoped-for Artemis crewed landings in 2024, these boxes could provide key insights on lunar resource viability and environmental attributes to aid future base planning.

The shoebox-sized Reactor On A Rover would fire neutrons into crater floors seeking hydrogen, a precious resource that could be harvested for astronaut life support systems and rocket fuel. The Near Surface Composition Mapper and Lunar Environment heliophysics package together aimed to add fresh details about regolith makeup and fluctuating temperature extremes. And the final two payloads focused on studying the moon's notoriously tricky lighting conditions - an Ultraviolet Imager to gauge sun damage risks on materials, and an Ambient Environment Particle Lunar Dust Analyzer to provide the first accurate measures of miniscule dusty sprays feared capable of compromising habitats and spacesuits if taken lightly.

Beyond NASA, a diverse makeup of commercial enterprises lined up for a spot inside Peregrine's cargo hold. Satellite telephony megacorp Intelsat booked delivery of a prototype communication dish promising lag-free broadband video relay from lunar surface to home basements back on Earth. Houston-based space startup Intuitive Machines chose Astrobotic for reliably planting their tiny hopping Nova-C rover, which may scout ice deposits inside dark craters. And Japanese enterprises iSpace and Sony rode aboard, risking a rugged external sensor package to capture 4K and 8K video of Peregrine's landing for marketing and R&D purposes.

Peregrine also carried education-minded payloads aiming to inspire future generations. Colorado school kids crafted inspiration plaques with artistic messages of unity. Pittsburgh high schoolers prepared biology experiments testing yeast cell gene expressions across lunar day cycles. University teams from Mexico and Guatemala collaborated on a robotic arm attachment to practice remote manipulation tasks across vast distances - skills integral for future lunar outpost construction and maintenance without humans present. And a new Los Alamos crystal detector design hitched a ride to gauge feasibility for deploying radiation sensors that might one day warn astronauts of approaching solar storms.

Nor were nations absent from Peregrine's manifest now that the moon again shaped geopolitics on Earth. Poland's space agency engineered the hardy Perfect Place habitat experiment testing 3D printed regolith radiation shielding techniques. A Czech OmniLight sensor package would measure 123 widespectrum variables over multiple frigid lunar nights, searching for evidence that plants might someday photosynthesize on the moon as ambitions for permanent bases soar. And carrying the banner for Luxembourg's rising space industry ambitions, an experimental electric rover company named SpaceForest strived to become the first private lunar rover ever independently operated remotely.

But perhaps most intriguing were two shoestring budget ARTMoon projects led by teams with no scientific background whatsoever. One endeavor launched a spherical titanium Time Capsule containing digital messages of peace from people worldwide (including global leaders) to rest undisturbed for generations.. The accompanying lunar library stored a solid state drive compilation of world literature classics and other prominent human artistic achievements onto the moon as a cultural backup. Both projects raised eyebrows for technical shakiness, but moved forward on artistic merits for their unity messaging.

Controversy struck late in the integration process when objections arose around two commercial space burial companies who paid to include symbolic amounts of participant ashes within commemorative payload spheres. While families found the notion of symbolically memorializing loved ones touching, some Native American tribes and religious groups strongly opposed treating such remains so cavalierly given the moon's sacred significance in their cultures. Out of sensitivity for indigenous concerns, NASA briefly weighed scrubbing the burial payload entirely before reaching an awkward compromise permitting only DNA samples instead of actual ashes.

By early 2024, Peregrine's cargo manifest encapsulated a globally crowd-sourced mix of commercial, government and education demonstration technologies rather than pure science. Not since Apollo 11's Flabége egg timer, gold olive branch, and homing patch has a vessel to Luna borne such quirky mementos and dreams alongside goods in service of commerce. Astrobotic hoped this diverse payload heritage just maybe, possibly, united humankind a bit more as our second great moon age dawned.

Chapter 6: Objections from Native Groups

Indigenous tribes across North America began voicing ethical objections in late 2023 to private space companies launching cremated human remains to rest on the lunar surface. Several Native American religious traditions hold sacred reverence for the moon as an spiritual entity or deity figure that animationally governs seasons, rhythms, and cycles on Mother Earth. Concerns heightened around NASA's revelation that an Astrobotic lunar lander contracted to deliver agency payloads would also carry memorial spaceflight participants from two companies catering to space burial industry interests.

Specifically, the issue was honoring celestial bodies as living forces of nature while also treating the moon as a dumping ground for mankind's deceased. "The very act devalues the sanctity of the Moon Mother to our people," declared Chief Lonnie Click of the Navajo

Nation Council. Other Southwestern U.S. tribes like Apache, Pueblo, Hopi and Zuni echoed similar grievances. Several nations called for peaceful protest demonstrations at regional NASA facilities and political intervention urging reconsideration.

Native protests aimed to sway more casual observers by invoking analogies to perceived desecrations of Indian burial grounds or sacred lands. But facile comparisons faltered outside tribal interests. For most public citizens and space advocates, centuries of Earthside imperialism and Manifest Destiny offered no bearing on leaving cremated remains respectfully on a barren satellite void of life, oxygen, or independent ontology. If anything the memorial tributes seemed poignant gestures celebrating lost family now symbolically soaring among the stars that awed them.

With the matter escalating towards a public relations dilemma, NASA administrator Bill Nelson proactively contacted Navajo Nation leadership indicating willingness for Astrobotic to consider modifying aspects of the space burial payloads. Nelson cited the agency's sensitivity to minority perspectives from past discrimination debacles while pledging to sustain constructive dialog. After all, no one disputed the moon's beauty and mystery as worth cherishing, however one's backgrounds or legends interpreted Luna's role in the cosmos. But Nelson firmly clarified NASA itself had no authority dictating terms for payloads launched commercially under FAA licenses rather than the agency's own oversight.

President Biden's advisors recommended against direct White House involvement in what seemed an edge culture war skirmish at first glance. But as moderate legislators and religious groups joined the rising chorus of bipartisan tribal backlash, Biden felt inclined towards symbolic reconciliation to preserve cooperation across so many constituencies key to his space exploration vision. Days before the rocket rollout, a rare weekend Camp David Summit convened with

Navajo leadership, space scientists, faith delegates, and astro-ethicists aiming to synthesize workable policy wisdom or guidelines for showing respect, restraint and reverence across mankind's expanding off-world footprint.

The rich but delicate dialogue yielded only broad advice - that outer space's bounty ever expands while sacrosanct landscapes grow only more vulnerable across time and tribes. All humanity shares stewardship duties for nurturing both frontier possibilities and precious planetary endowments like no other among the stars. Participants committed optimistically towards partnering on forging co-stewardship principles that fairly weigh profound moral obligations owed both the living and the deceased.

In practice however, with launch fast-approaching no tangible consensus emerged on whether memorial spaceflights should proceed, pause for vetting frameworks, or cancel outright. Rather an ambiguous document of lofty prose dynamically "committed to committing towards a committing" at later times. With global spotlight glaring pressure, the summit's clunky outcome largely kicked the can down the road. But it vitally connected tribal stakeholders into policy conversations where they demanded respected voices on space decisions touching heritage concerns. The seeds for molding nascent off-world governance germinated, even if growth curves remained long-term.

In the near-term vacuum of actionable direction, the FAA ultimately followed NASA's lead in punting the payload decision fully to Astrobotic's discretion. Legal liability belonged to the startup anyway as payload provider rather than the launch services company United Launch Alliance. Astrobotic CEO John Thornton still scrambled up to the eve of flight preparations with tribal leaders earnestly seeking amenable compromise. Sympathetic to their spiritual stance from a position of reverence, he floated guaranteed future Peregrine mission seats for native ashes at no cost. But offering exclusivity rightly provoked backlash that the moon should remain beyond transactional exploitation.

With no perfect options, Astrobotic reluctantly backed NASA's preference for flying DNA samples to acknowledge loss for affected families rather than nix tributes outright. Far from an elegant solution, ambiguous order out of public pressures still furnished private cover. The unsatisfying result left all sides equally uncomfortable as the Vulcan Centaur rocket at last heaved Peregrine heavenward without answers, only openness that the longer path towards ethically cohabitating worlds old and new demanded many humble first footsteps not yet seen.

Chapter 7: ULA Bets Big on Vulcan

Though NASA furnished top billing for Peregrine's history-making lunar voyage, an equally monumental yet overlooked engineering feat made headlines that dawned - the maiden flight of United Launch Alliance's next-generation Vulcan Centaur rocket. After decades reliably serving US military and aerospace customers, ULA's leadership gambled their company's future on the success of this new vehicle they hoped could compete with rival SpaceX and other newcomers.

Ever since ULA formed in 2006 as a joint venture between legacy rocket giants Boeing and Lockheed Martin, the Atlas V operated as the fledgling firm's workhorse vehicle. Alongside the Delta IV lineup, Atlas furnished critical liftoff capability for dozens of high-value national security satellites until the 2020s. But both vehicle families relied upon increasingly uncertified Russian-supplied RD-180 main engines that powered their first stages. Given worsening foreign relations, ULA's dependence grew untenable.

Worse still, disruptive forces shook the entire commercial launch sector as Elon Musk's scrappy SpaceX pioneered rocket reusability techniques that slashed operational costs. ULA's sterling reputation meant little next to rivals promising equivalent reliability at half the price. Icy Pentagon board rooms warned that America ceding launch market dominance posed strategic threats. ULA suddenly confronted an existential crisis - adapt quickly or fade away within the decade.

With the crisis came opportunity. ULA CEO Tory Bruno envisioned a clean-sheet next-generation rocket leveraging new American-built engines that could recapture medium-lift leadership. By starting from scratch, they could optimize every engineering trade-off rather than incrementally alter legacy vehicles. What emerged from their Hawthorne design shop was an all-new Vulcan Centaur rocket that could lift over 50,000 lbs into low-Earth orbit while incorporating partial reusability.

Bruno knew that just matching SpaceX on specs wouldn't suffice given their billion dollar head start. Instead he had to leverage ULA's reliability record, manufacturing excellence and customer intimacy as competitive advantages no upstart could equal overnight. That meant limiting vulnerabilities through tremendous systems engineering prowess, mission assurance and parts commonality. Vulcan's five primary configurations ensured ULA could tailor to diverse customer needs more responsively. And a focus on rapid payload processing and launch-day readiness promised significantly lower overhead costs even if booster recovery took years to attempt.

Structurally, Vulcan Centaur built upon the Atlas V's proven cryogenic upper stage which employed liquid methane and oxygen to generate thrust in vacuum after initial liftoff. But absent imported Russian engines, ULA contracted Jeff Bezos' secretive Blue Origin to design a new powerful BE-4 engine that utilized liquified natural gas. Providing equivalent thrust at much lower cost than rival Aerojet Rocketdyne's AR-1 concept, two BE-4s arranged at Vulcan's base would ignite alongside twin solid rocket boosters for initial ascent. Once MECO occurred minutes later, only the Centaur upper stage continued firing to push payloads to orbital velocity or interplanetary trajectories.

Ambitiously, ULA aimed not just to fly Vulcan but to advance American manufacturing by domesticating the full supply chain using advanced techniques like metal 3D printing of parts. Their goal to spur a " combustion renaissance" would incubate invaluable skills for realizing the full potential of methane rocket propulsion. Bezos shared this vision for Blue

Origin's BE-4 production facilities in Alabama and Florida to create high-tech aerospace hubs rivaling old Space Coast legacies. Succeeding with Vulcan offered macroeconomic benefits that promised to inspire a new generation towards space.

But theory alone couldn't launch payloads to orbit. After years of concepting in simulations, ULA's team had to translate dreams into buildable hardware. Midway through the decade Boeing and Lockheed doubled down on sharing the financial risk after an initial DARPA development partnership expired. Fabricating booster cores, welding-testing cryogenic tanks, cold-firing those BE-4 methane engines and pushing the towering rocket through meticulous Systems Integration Lab testing consumed five years and over $2 billion before Vulcan stood ready to fly.

Debut preparations flowed towards an unusually tense crescendo because so much hinged on success. Failure would produce hair-trigger

Pentagon demands to accelerate SpaceX's alternative rockets as backup. And the symbolism of new American-sourced engines stumbling in their first real test could shake Congress' willingness to appropriate ongoing funds. Against the backdrop of renewed space race dynamics, Vulcan's inaugural launch commenced with almost as much national anticipation as the SLS Artemis 1 flight the prior year.

As the countdown clock expired, Vulcan's engines ignited with a brilliant flash that bathed the predawn Florida coastline in light. Crowds along beachside causeways whooped cheers that carried aloft across the bellowing rocket trailing fiery plumes. ULA's Company future now rode skyward atop a gusher of raw hydrocarbon energy destined to propel Peregrine towards the lunar frontier. After flawless mission completion minutes later, focus rightly centered on the moon landing attempt ahead. But ULA won its own giant leap forward that night towards securing domestic space leadership for years ahead.

Chapter 8: Liftoff At Last

Pitch darkness enveloped Cape Canaveral in the wee hours of January 8th, 2024, offering little hint of the rocket now looming just miles offshore upon a concrete launch pedestal surrounded by open water. Shrouded in inky Atlantic mists, the slender Vulcan Centaur stood 17 stories tall, crowned by the conical nose cone sheltering Astrobotic's Peregrine lander. Days earlier this towering new workhorse of American spaceflight completed rollout from ULA's complex 41 integration building before robotic transport to this riverside launchpad.

Tonight's planned launch marked the first attempted flight not only for Vulcan Centaur, but also for several onboard systems working in unison for the first time operationally. Namely, software managing the BE-4 engines, avionics packages translating inertial guidance commands, and launch vehicle flight termination hardware had logged countless simulation hours but zero live test experience until now. Myriad metrics across so many unprecedented rocket and payload elements inevitably elevated risk calculations beyond standard debut discomfort. But such was the burden ambitious new space frontiers shouldered after decades spent refining existing vehicle families in orbit.

For United Launch Alliance leadership like CEO Tory Bruno overseeing tonight's launch operations, success now hung by a thread. The Pentagon specifically commissioned this lunar lander demonstration hoping to accelerate pathways for commercially ferrying defense prototypes to lunar surface outposts under Project Vanguard. Failure jeopardized national security validation critical for justifying full funding tranches Congress planned debating in coming months. And beyond financial impacts, missed Vulcan Centaur launch targets or reliability shortfalls amplified fears that upstart rivals like SpaceX or Blue Origin's mammoth

New Glenn rocket might continue eating into ULA market share across the 2030s.

The boosters were visibly "pumped" walking room to room inside ULA Mission Control. Years of design prototyping, test stand firings, systems integration testing, procedural rehearsals.. it had all led to tonight. VIPs representing Boeing, Lockheed Martin, DARPA, Intelsat, and assorted military bigwigs filed quietly into the viewing auditorium lining back rows to avoid crowding Bruno's focus upfront. NASA leadership joined virtually to observe Peregrine's ride to destiny. As countdown clocks flashed crimson, scores of engineers peered intently into diagnostic monitor arrays hoping calibrations illuminated green across the board.

Out on Cape Canaveral's darkened coastline, obstructed views left crowds relying on external PA narration echoing for miles. Huddled masses braved pre-dawn inland chill for precious glimpses through the hazy night. Skeptical murmurs noted someone's large drone illegally hovering too low, before realizing that the bright orb visible drifting overhead wasn't the moon but Vulcan itself illuminated against cloud backs. Officials cleared launch photographer sites nearest the pad, calming restless onlookers with assurances of imminent ignition.

Back inside Mission Control, propellant loading commenced around 2:30 AM through twin umbilicals that snaked across launch platform decks now retracting in final sequences. Liquid oxygen chilled to near-cryogenic temperature -300°F first flowed into upper stage tanks, followed by trickles of liquid methane and hydrogen. Pressure and stability cues rang acceptable as anticipation swelled. This was no simulation anymore - Peregrine and her payloads now entrusted their fates astride real volatile forces that harnessing controlled power alone separated triumph from tragedy.

Public officials stepped forth blessing the launch event with remarks extolling American engineering prowess towards uninhibited horizons, before ceding the communications loop fully to Bruno's capable voice. Grizzled launch veterans agreed ULA's rocket boss exuded uncommon calm and command even facing multiplied scrutiny this night. Confidence gained from operating 190 launches couldn't fully explain Bruno's aura that Vulcan's eventual flight would take care of external pressures - "We just need to fly our plan."

With five minutes left, the definitive launch commit was confirmed. Vulcan Centaur's autonomous self-check monitoring would govern all critical "go/no go" decisions from here forward faster than humans could process or override anyway. Eerie quiet descended across the control room as everyone unconsciously leaned forwards, feeling the moment's simulation ever replicated. Each mind ticked down personal clocks timed to their specialty's moments of peak performance anxiety ahead - telemetry teams, hydraulics monitors, electrical engineers, debris experts, cooling specialists, pressurization leads - all narrowed intense focus before the imminent spark.

Murmured status check-ins aloud for team situational awareness broke tense silence. Fuel levels are good. Guidance in sync. Thrust vector responding. Weather remains green. At T-60 seconds, the fire door swung shut on Peregrine's pristine Centaur payload shroud. What little outside chatter remained quickly hushed. Knuckles whitened gripping armrests. Breaths unconsciously held. Here we go...

T-minus 10... 9... Final engine start sequence begins... 7...6...
Valves wide...4...3... Turbopumps igniting... 2...1... We have engine start and liftoff! Hold parameters... Clamps released... Vulcan Centaur now airborne on first flight!... Cameras confirmed a good flight profile...

Departing crowds roared seeing the night sky disabled by a blinding fury of orange and yellow flames as Vulcan Centaur cleared the pad.

Trailing four billowing exhaust plumes stretching 140 feet behind, the slender rocket climbed faster than seemed possible. Shockwaves rumbled through beachside parking lots like cannon blasts, resonating off chest walls despite miles of buffer distance. Tracker cameras tracked rocket rise towards thinning clouds until the glowing plume pierced a gap. Jaws clenched in anticipation of staging events still minutes away...

Inside mission control, delirious engineers traded giddy handshakes and backslaps as years of shared identity sacrifice now propelled beyond any more meddling. But laser eyes never wandered long from blinking monitors as their beast now flew beyond reach. Fingers hovered keyboards ready to respond if discordant alarms triggered. For now though, all indications confirmed Vulcan Centaur remained right on trajectory for her spacefaring destiny.

Tonight, fortunes changed and futures took flight on pillars of flame receding from view off

Florida's coast. Where Peregrine and those long-awaited BE-4 engines might steer their missions only time would reveal. But in this gleaming moment modern titans once again forged technological wonders rivaling old Apollo feats - no mere nostalgia act, but a canvas awaiting humanity's ambitions to script new space histories unimagined.

Chapter 9: The Flight to Luna

Minutes after watching Vulcan Centaur successfully deliver Peregrine to low Earth orbit, the mood inside Astrobotic's modest Pittsburgh headquarters swelled with relief and rising confidence. Eight years of setbacks, fundraising struggles, technical delays had all culminated towards this historic launch. Now their squat minimalist lander buoyed by ambition alone coasted nearly 200 miles overhead at 17,000 mph while Florida receded fast in the rear view. Even so, the team understood their real trial only commenced having crossed the survivable atmosphere boundary inescapably tethering all terrestrial things.

To escape Earth's gravitational pull, Peregrine next had to ignite her cruise stage engines on the opposite side from Florida some 45 minutes later. If that critical Trans Lunar Injection burn failed, the spacecraft would simply swing back around helpless on some wayward orbit awaiting demise. But right on schedule, telemetry screens lit up as planned. The lander's communication dishes realigned sunward to contact ground stations in Australia confirming a good burn. Pings received from Peregrine's medium gain antenna carried the first notes of celebration in Pittsburgh - they were moonbound at last.

The three day coast phase ahead promised little drama, but immense anticipation as NASA's own CAPSTONE probe had reminded all last year. Deep space journeying exposed vessels to all manner of structural and electrical vulnerabilities absent within the protective atmosphere. Thankfully, Peregrine's compact robust design traded radiation hardening and thicker shielding over minimalist propulsion needs for this one-way descent. Barring any unseen micrometeoroid impacts disabling vital equipment, confidence ran high on safe transit.

Yet payload teams sweated the free cruise more than Astrobotic engineers. None could venture mid-course corrections if payload vibrations exceeded tested levels. The lander's spartan unpressurized compartment offered no climate controlled comfort for customers' tech experiments vulnerable to the harsh void. Companies like Intelsat carefully crafted secondary containment vessels, insulation jacketing, and shock absorbing mounts to secure their prototypes. But analog testing never quite matched actual launch dynamics or thermally-stressed rigor. Incoming telemetry needed constant monitoring to detect any payload anomalies early.

NASA's payload engineers overseeing the agency's five delivered science packages breathed easier knowing their instruments passed initial post-launch checkouts. Toughened for space resilience from decades perfecting durable technology, these shoebox-sized investigations tolerated extreme environments better than commercial prototypes. Big isotropic challenges now involved properly coordinating sleep versus active states across the two week cruise to conserve limited battery reserves. Too little juice for surface examination and sensors couldn't fulfill mission promises.

For Pittsburgh's small Astrobotic team, the week ahead encouraged rest before terminal landing phase cacophony. Barring any wake up alarms, their watchful role mainly involved ensuring ground dish connectivity handoffs went smoothly between various Earth tracking stations. Confidence in the software programmed for autonomous control justified lighter staffing demands. And so a slightly muted celebration continued as engineers dispersed for respite from the relentless pressure cooker intensity of final launch preps.

Equilibrium restored, a brief quiet period of anticipation took hold. Far beyond tireless planning measures, ultimate success hinged on forces indifferent to mankind's yearning. The young faces that conceived Peregrine over dorm room beers long ago overheard nocturnal whispers from the ancient Sea of Tranquility now 200,000 miles below. Her fortunes beckoned ahead through the timeless cosmic veil shrouding fickle Luna's nearside plains. Fortunes favors the bold, or the patient, or neither, or both.

Nine days later as scheduled, Peregrine's guidance thrusters fired to slow orbital velocity and settle into a perilously low nine mile polar orbit around the Moon. Visiting this lunar graveyard spelled doom for most man made objects. But tonight it facilitated honing targeting solutions for the landing ahead. After methodically assessing slopes, crater rims, boulders and shadows, Peregrine's LIDAR systems selected a smooth Mare Imbrium plain right of the lava-carved 25 mile wide Lambert Rille gorge.

Having synthesized a navigation solution, Peregrine next had to ignite her main descent engine at precisely the right instant. Earlier she crashes into the lunar mountains. Late and she overshoots the far horizon. On touchdown minus 26 hours, computers initiated the do-or-die Powered Descent Initiation burn. Cameras related slowing imagery back to Earth as apparent surface features gradually enlarged. Topographic sensors triple checked clearance across the heart-stopping plunge towards regolith less than three football fields below before engines finally cut out. Now gravity alone dragged Peregrine into her fate…

Chapter 10: Touchdown

A tense quiet pervaded Astrobotic's mission control as clocks counted down to Peregrine's long-awaited touchdown attempt. Despite flawless performance getting the spacecraft this far, disaster potentially lurked mere seconds away. 15 years of setbacks and financial struggles would mean nothing if Peregrine crashed now. And with the entire process automated hundreds of thousands of miles away, engineers in this room couldn't tweak trajectory or thrust if anything looked off nominal. Their hopes rode fully on software and sensors functioning free of errors.

It had been a long road since the origins of Astrobotic's scrappy lunar ambitions among college students in Pittsburgh. After years of bootstrapping milestones through prizes and partnerships, this NASA contract's chance to deliver agency payloads to Oceanus Procellarum seemed like their big break. But actually producing a flight-ready lander on a lean budget confronted setbacks at every turn. Just qualifying Peregrine's guidance systems and hazard avoidance algorithms for operational certifications nearly bankrupted the startup more than once.

Yet giving up would have dashed the dream forever. Astrobotic's crew found the grit to pull through late stage technical challenges with Peregrine time and again - weld defects around the thrust nozzles, integration delays with the flight termination system, damaged shock absorbers in that off-nominal drop test. Each week brought make-or-break Weyland-Yutani pressure. But finally years behind schedule, their inelegant yet capable lander stood ready to survive the ultimate unforgiving exam.

Scores of company employees, investors, and family packed conference rooms to share in the imminent moment. Screen views switched between Peregrine's rapidly descending external camera feeds, 3D surface projection models, instrument panel telemetry, and anxious faces hovering mission control technicians. Despite attempts masking tension with optimistic banter, the entire scene felt balanced on knife's edge. In mere minutes, collective fates would crystallize one way or another.

Unlike Apollo's manned descents long ago, no crackling radio transmissions connected Peregrine's final harrowing plunge towards the pitted lunar surface. Instead near panicked silence prevailed save for digitized descent stage computer calls. Altitude and velocity metrics ticked lower in bold font - 3000 feet... 2600 feet... 45 seconds to contact... 1900 feet, engines cut... brace for impact! Reassuringly all lights flashed green as the four spindly landing legs unfurled into tripod configuration like some alien lunar insect.

At just 40 feet, puffs burst across the regolith indicating successful pre-contact propellant dispersal to minimize dust blowback. Drift remained under 2 mph well within stability bounds. This was really going to happen! Cameras could discern pebbles and cracks now as seconds out anxiety reached a fever pitch crescendo. Hearts raced with baited breath witnessing this audacious dream a scrappy startup chased ridiculed for nearly two decades was impossibly... actually...going...to...

Contact. Touchdown Confirmed! Screams and shouts immediately erupted from employees with tears flowing as years of stressful toil culminated in this glorious vindication of ultimate underdog triumph. All telemetry nail'd stable as cheers soon turned to awestruck hugs hardly believing Peregrine now rested upon the same lunar mare which captivated imaginations since boyhood. Champagne corks echoed distinctly audible through the video feed static. Back Slaps abounded as months of lingering nervous energy released at once in communal relief. They had done it - the first ever privately funded soft landing of a spacecraft on the lunar frontier. Crash ceilings and make history indeed!

Word spread quickly as NASA officials raced across halls to congratulate the small Pittsburgh team which, against all odds, somehow managed to beat the agency back to Luna with a spunky little lander full of dreams. Social media lit ablaze as analysts immediately recognized the significance of this milestone extending beyond engineering accolades. For the promise of Artemis now involved far more human destinies converging upon Luna than solely tax-sponsored astronaut sorties to plant flags anew. Indeed, toute suite companies like Intuitive Machines and won landing contracts from NASA, delivering their first CLPS payloads soon after.

In the months following Peregrine's inaugural touchdown, demand for Astrobotic's delivery services to the moon accelerated rapidly. Requests to fly experimental payloads delivered by Griffin landers stacked up from companies and universities worldwide. Off-world enterprise more broadly captured global imagination as the realities of practicing lunar commerce and tourism came into focus. America proudly reclaimed the so-called "high moral ground" as private space startups charted the future rather than state agencies focused on symbolic Apollo throwbacks.

The irrepressible human longing to reach just beyond grasp awakened again seeing tireless dreams take flight. And much like those early daring Wright Brothers, the Astrobotic team's humble yet trailblazing success showed again howvalor bridges ambition to achievement across starry skies. Now more clearly than in decades, revived planetary exploration spirit once more summoned human imagination to expand frontiers of the possible.

Made in the USA
Monee, IL
08 May 2024

58156480R00039